Dr. Frank's
No-Aging Diet
Cookbook

Dr. Frank's
No-Aging Diet Cookbook

Barbara Friedlander and Marilyn Petersen

Foreword by
Benjamin S. Frank, M.D.

The Dial Press
New York
1977

Published by
The Dial Press
1 Dag Hammarskjold Plaza
New York, New York 10017

Book design by Elaine Golt Gongora

Manufactured in the United States of America

First printing

Library of Congress Cataloging in Publication Data

Friedlander, Barbara.
   Dr. Frank's no-aging diet cookbook.

   Includes index.
   1. Diet. 2. Cookery. 3. Longevity. 4. Nucleic acids—Therapeutic use. I. Petersen, Marilyn, 1928– joint author. II. Frank, Benjamin S., 1923–
III. Title. IV. Title: No-aging diet cookbook.
RA784.F74   613.2   77-5050
ISBN 0-8037-1958-2

This book is dedicated to Dr. Marvin Lifschitz

Acknowledgments

The authors would like to thank Herbert I. Cohen for generously supplying them with a variety of Empress sardines and to I. Epstein & Sons for their contribution of sardines for testing recipes. Thanks also to Jan L. Petersen for her assistance.

Contents

Foreword

We Americans are aging much too soon. Thanks to the triumphs of modern medicine, we are being kept alive longer—but in poor health. Fading eyesight, dimming mental functions, heart disease, emphysema, arthritis—these are only a few of the diseases which, tragically, we regard as perfectly natural for old people to suffer, along with loss of energy and sallow, wrinkled skin.

There is an easy and, as you will soon see, very pleasant way to delay this kind of aging. The way is through nutrition. It is now possible to maintain, even to regain, a good measure of youthfulness and vital energy far into advanced age.

I have made a discovery about nutrition. It seems so obvious to me as a scientist that I am puzzled that nutritionists have not investigated it long ago, but they are beginning to do so now. Thousands of my patients are in dramatically better health because of it.

For you this book can be a giant step toward a healthier, longer life. It is an excellent companion to my own book, *Dr. Frank's No-Aging Diet,* which I wrote with Philip Miele. While my book presents the diet, as this does, and provides some recipes, it describes my nutritional theory in more detail. This book presents an amazing variety of fascinating recipes. I have reviewed all of them and can attest to their nutritional value, though I want you to be very careful about any salt called for, as you should be with most recipes in other cookbooks. You would be wise to get used to using less salt than is common in the American diet. And for those who want to use sardines as recommended, there are excellent low-salt sardines on the market, as those who have been enjoying them for years can testify.

As you know, there are diets and there are diets. Most of them are for weight reduction. Some are for specific diseases. Quite a number burst forth as fads and soon disappear. Some are cause for serious concern within the medical profession. This diet is entirely different. It is a balanced diet. Its emphasis is more on what you should eat than on what you should not eat. It is fairly low in salt and moderately low in calories. Most important, it is safe; it provides more nutrition, not less.

Of course, if you are on some special regimen prescribed by your physician, you should check this diet with him beforehand. He may not yet agree with me on its benefits, but if he is at all open-minded he will not disagree. More important, he will almost surely tell you it is a balanced, healthy diet.

In a way, I regret calling this a diet. The word suggests a troublesome way of eating for some joyless period of time. My diet, particularly with these recipes, can make your meals more interesting and, once you feel its benefits, will become a valued part of your way of life.

A few words on how it works: Its key feature is that it is rich in nucleic acids. These are essential to the proper working of all the cells in our bodies. Most cells, as you know, reproduce themselves by dividing. How often they divide to form new ones, and the quality of these new ones, is determined by the amount and quality of nucleic acids available to them.

It is well known that our bodies make their own nucleic acids. This fact perhaps more than any other has led nutritionists to ignore the value of nucleic acids in foods. However, I believe that as we age, the enzymes and related materials involved in making nucleic acids become defective. Our cells themselves become defective. As they reproduce, the new cells inherit these defects and add new ones. This is old age.

However, when we eat nucleic acid−rich foods, our digestion breaks the acids down into their components. Our cells, then, with more raw materials to work with, put these components back together again and repair themselves. Vigorous cell repair reverses the effects of degenerative disease. In other words, cell repair is de-aging. This, grossly oversimplified, is the crux of my theory.

Some other theory, perhaps a totally different one, may turn up someday to account for the de-aging effect of my diet. No matter; from your point of view, what counts is that the diet works. There will be a new spring in your step, and you will look and feel younger because you will be healthier.

Benjamin S. Frank, M.D.

Part One

Dr. Frank's
NO-AGING DIET

The Diet

Since the beginning of time people have been looking for the fountain of youth, trying to discover the miraculous place or ingredient that would keep their bodies and minds young. What we seldom realize is that it has always been at hand; in fact, no further away than the food we eat. Anyone can partake of the miracle who is willing to take personal responsibility for his or her own health and well-being.

The first step in taking this responsibility is to approach the organism as a whole. When one views the body in this manner, it becomes obvious that disease is symptomatic of general imbalance, and to be effective any treatment should take into account root causes. Present medical practice tends to treat symptoms rather than causes and to treat isolated ailments rather than the entire interdependent organism—which often serves to arrest the ailment but does not reverse it or prevent its recurrence.

General health is also affected by mental attitude and physical exercise, as well as diet. A program of improved nutrition, exercise, fresh air, and positive attitudes may not only result in a state of better overall health but often in specific improvement of such conditions as poor gums and impaired eyesight. This is not really surprising—by treating the whole person one is also treating the individual parts. This diet goes even further: It provides a program which actually may *prevent* degenerative diseases associated with aging—by treating them *before* they start.

Dr. Benjamin S. Frank, whose theory and practice over the past twenty-five years inspired this book, believes that the key to aging and its concomitant degenerative diseases lies in the degree of health of the body's cells. Within the cell is the blueprint for all life. The more energy present in the cell the more efficiently it reproduces. This blueprint for healthy cell production and reproduction depends on cell nourishment, which is derived from food acted on by the digestive enzymes.

Some of the enzymes present in the small intestine break food down into molecules known as nucleic acid and related materials. Nucleic acid is essential to life. There are two major types of nucleic acids: deoxyribonucleic acid (DNA), which carries the information for the formation and reproduction of living cells, and ribonucleic acid (RNA), which puts this information into action. Nucleic acid can also be produced from several dietary components. However, for optimum levels, additional nucleic acid must be obtained from specific foods that are high in the substance. Without this supplementation various diseases and degeneration of the organism which we have come to accept as the natural aging process are more likely to manifest themselves.

Put very simply, extra nourishment of the cells by a diet high in nucleic acid slows down the aging process and in many instances can revitalize and repair already existing infirmities. There also seems to be some correlation between how well a cell utilizes oxygen and the health of the cell. Nucleic acid permits the body to perform better with less oxygen and to make more efficient use of available oxygen. Furthermore (and possibly most important), the supplementation of nucleic acid in the diet through foods recommended in Dr. Frank's No-Aging Diet is safe, without side effects, inexpensive, and as easy and pleasurable as the act of eating every day.

HOW TO LOOK AND FEEL YOUNG

One of the most visible indications of organ malfunction or deterioration and aging is in the appearance of the skin, particularly of the face. This diet is for everyone's face. In a young person adolescent acne is usually a symptom of some internal disorder; as one grows older dry skin and eventually wrinkles and deep lines may appear. The condition of one's skin cannot be viewed as something separate and apart, but rather as a reflection of one's general health. As a diet high in nucleic acid nourishes every cell in the body, the skin (its largest organ) often responds quickly and dramatically. Acne clears up, lines and wrinkles diminish, dry skin becomes moist, and oily skin dries out. The loose skin common in middle age tightens up, creating a more youthful apppearance. The truth of the matter is that the person *is* more youthful.

Nucleic acid augments more efficient reproduction of normal cell structure. Weaker reproduction results in the signs of aging. Let's use the example of a copying machine: Although the original print may be perfect (as our cells are at birth), if the inking process is inferior, each copy will be fainter and fainter (the nourishment is the ink). Nucleic acid, then, is the key to healthier cell reproduction.

Naturally, the older someone looks the more dramatic the improvement. However, one need not wait for that. This diet can be valuable in prevention as well as treatment. Younger people need never experience those signs of aging we've come to take for granted. Also, in view of the characteristics of nucleic acid, Dr. Frank has found that a diet high in nucleic acid is effective in treating such diseases and conditions as emphysema, heart disease, diabetic complications, arthritis, fading eyesight, loss of memory, effects of drug addiction and alcoholism, acne, and a host of infirmities attributable to old age.

One of the advantages of this diet is that its restrictions are minimal. Its value depends on what you do eat rather than on what you don't. The foods are easily obtainable even in a restaurant.

RULES OF THE DIET

1. Four days a week eat a three- or four-ounce can of small sardines. (Drain the oil if you're concerned about your weight, or use sardines packed in water with no salt added.)

2. One other day have salmon (canned or fresh) as a main course.

3. On still another day have shrimp, lobster, squid, clams, or oysters as a main course.

4. On the remaining day eat any other kind of fish as a main course.

In other words, you must have fish seven times a week—sardines four times, salmon once, nonvertebrate seafood once, and any other kind of fish once.

5. Have calf liver once a week.

6. Once a week have beets, beet juice, or borscht.

7. Once or twice a week have a side dish of lentils, peas, lima beans, or soybeans.

8. Each day eat at least one of the following: asparagus, radishes, onions, scallions, mushrooms, spinach, cauliflower, or celery.

9. Each day have one strong multivitamin after any meal (therapeutic strength).

10. Each day drink two glasses of skim milk.*

11. Each day drink a glass of fruit or vegetable juice.

12. Each day drink at least four glasses of water—more in the summer to replace perspiration.

Items 10, 11, and 12 must never be omitted. These fluids prevent the urine from becoming acidic, which can cause problems with kidney stones or gout. If you are conscientious about fluids, you will have no problem with kidney stones. If, however, you suffer from gout, the diet can be very beneficial providing you maintain close medical supervision to keep the uric acid level down.† Those with

---

* If preferred, water may be substituted, in addition to the four glasses recommended in step 12.

† Black cherry juice is very beneficial for gout sufferers.

hypertension, heart disease, or other conditions where salt intake should be kept very low are advised to use salt-free varieties of sardines, salmon, and other foods.

Ginseng

Ginseng has long been considered a panacea by the Oriental countries, as its name, Panax Ginseng, suggests (*panax* from the Greek, meaning "all-healing," and *ginseng* from the Chinese *shen seng,* meaning "man-root"). The western world did for a time use ginseng pharmacologically, but since the 1960s has viewed the root primarily as an exotic aphrodisiac. The true value of ginseng seems to lie somewhere between the two.

Recent investigations by American and Soviet researchers have brought to light much information affirming the ancient mystique of ginseng. So far the results of this research indicate that the root can be classified as an adaptogen, in that it increases the general resistance to disease without deleterious side effects. Of particular importance for this book, however, is the effect ginseng has on RNA/DNA production. Animal experiments disclose that ginseng accelerates synthesis of DNA in skin cells, stimulates RNA synthesis in liver cells, expedites DNA synthesis in lymphocytes under normal and stress conditions, increases RNA/DNA content of adrenal cells, and enhances formation of ATP. These effects on cellular metabolism are responsible for the adaptogenic influence of ginseng.

Dr. Frank states that ginseng enhances the effects of a diet rich in nucleic acid and stimulates the production of nucleic acid in the cells.

Ginseng is widely available in Oriental food stores as well as health food stores. The most common forms are capsules, packets of tea, and extract. Dr. Frank recommends the extract for its higher potency. It is a dark, gooey substance that comes in a small bottle. A tiny plastic spoon is usually included. One tiny spoonful dissolved in hot water and taken as a beverage once or twice a day is suggested. The taste is strange at first, but one does develop a liking for it after a few tries. It reminds some people of black coffee with a slightly bitter aftertaste. Ginseng in powder form is encased in gelatin capsules. The tea is usually composed of tiny crystals that dissolve instantly in hot water. Although not as potent as the extract, it is a very pleasant beverage and much milder tasting than the extract. Many people enjoy both the tea and the extract sweetened with a little honey (ginseng should never be stirred with any metal except silver—wood or plastic is preferred).

The ancient regard for ginseng is now being noted with greater respect by the western world. It is generally agreed that the healthier you are the sexier you are, and here East meets West.

NUTRITIONAL RULES FOR VEGETARIANS

Each meal must include at least one of the first three combinations:

1. Grains with milk products
2. Legumes (beans, peas, lentils) with grains
3. Nuts and seeds with legumes
4. Asparagus three times a week
5. Mushrooms three times a week
6. Beets, beet juice, or borscht three times a week
7. Collard greens, cauliflower, spinach, soybean sprouts, or turnip greens as part of your main meal, four times a week

Every day you must have:

8. A glass of fruit or vegetable juice
9. Two glasses of skim milk (water, fruit, or vegetable juice may be substituted)

10. At least four glasses of water

11. One therapeutic-strength vitamin tablet with main meal

If you are willing to eat fish, follow the regular diet but replace liver with any fish.

The recipes in this book have been designed to provide you with a simple and delicious way to incorporate nucleic acid into your diet. The section on Vegetables, Grains, and Legumes (pages 117–141) will be of particular interest to vegetarians. Although this is not a restrictive diet, we have not included recipes for other foods, such as muscle meats, roasts, and stews. However, we recommend as natural a diet as possible. This precludes the use of refined products like white flour and sugar, excessive salt, and foods containing chemical additives, artificial flavorings and colorings, and preservatives.

Vegetables and fruits should be bought fresh rather than canned or frozen, and, if possible, they should be organically grown without chemical fertilizers and pesticides and not treated with preservatives. Foods untainted by these substances are not only healthier but noticeably better-tasting.

Produce is often waxed, dyed, or sprayed to preserve its shelf life and fresh look. If you do not grow your own vegetables or find it too difficult to obtain them from organic sources, make sure they are thoroughly scrubbed and rinsed (vinegar or salt in water will remove some residue of sprays). Generally, vegetables should be eaten unpeeled to take full advantage of their vitamin and mineral content, but wax and dye are difficult to remove and vegetables so treated should be peeled.

We believe the disadvantages of eating meat far outweigh the advantages, because of the high concentrations of hormones and antibiotics with which cattle and chickens are injected. These substances can be harmful to our health since they bring about undesirable chemical changes and affect our resistance to disease. However, many people like meat, and therefore we suggest that you try to buy meat and poultry from sources that certify it to be organically fed and free of hormones and antibiotics. Those people who must be cautious of cholesterol levels and sodium intake should generally avoid eating meat. And for everyone, eating meat occasionally instead of daily is preferable.

We have included some interesting recipes for liver and poultry. We have excluded recipes for other meats, as these abound elsewhere and we do not wish to be repetitious. Calf liver is preferred to steer liver because there are less toxins in the younger animal. Although it is very rich in nucleic acid, it should not be eaten more than once a week because of the high cholesterol content. Chicken and turkey may also be used to vary the diet, and it should be noted that the dark meat is higher in nucleic acid than the white meat.

Thanks to researchers like Dr. Benjamin S. Frank, the infirmities of old age do not have to be assumed to be our natural birthright. We can truly grow old with health, energy, and zest for life. To lead a long and vigorous life need no longer be considered exceptional. If we take more responsibility for our health, if we are open to new knowledge on nutrition, this ideal may well be within everyone's reach.

Special Ailments and RNA

The following information should be of dietary help to those with special problems. It is wise, however, for those in good health to follow the advice of Dr. Frank and other doctors on the question of sodium intake: Try to cut the amount of salt you ordinarily use and even eliminate it altogether when at all possible. In those recipes where "salt to taste" is called for, use the good judgment of your doctor and your own good sense: Try to do without salt. Cut the amount of salt in half if a quantity is given, if you are at all able. A cut lemon (fresh) on the table is a good substitute for salt. Consult your doctor on the various non-sodium salt substitutes available in supermarkets and health food stores.

Osteoarthritis

If you have a mild case or a family history of osteoarthritis, the following supplements to the diet will be very helpful:

1. Take one or two teaspoons of brewer's yeast (dissolved in fruit or vegetable juice) daily. After a few days increase to one tablespoon per day. This is very high in nucleic acid and B vitamins.

2. Take one tablespoon of blackstrap molasses per day.

3. Take one tablespoon of wheat germ daily.

4. Use honey instead of sugar; honey has manganese, which helps build joint tissue.

5. Avoid all citrus fruit and juice.

6. In addition to a therapeutic-strength vitamin tablet, take 250 milligrams of pantothenic acid and 250 milligrams of vitamin C two times daily with meals.

This regimen will not cure a severe case of arthritis, but with the help of a physician it may alleviate the symptoms.

It will, however, noticeably reduce the symptoms of a mild case.

Diabetes

Along with the usual dietary restrictions and medications, other supplements can also be most helpful. In addition to a therapeutic-strength multivitamin tablet, take a strong B-complex tablet, one teaspoon of soy lecithin, and one tablespoon of brewer's yeast daily increased to two after a few weeks.

Breathing Difficulties

One of the qualities of a diet high in nucleic acid plus vitamin supplements is its assistance in the increased utilization of available oxygen. Nucleic acid therapy has proven effective for many of Dr. Frank's patients in the relief of the symptoms of emphysema and chronic bronchitis. This therapy will not cure these diseases, but because the body can perform better with less oxygen, an alleviation of shortness of breath can be expected. Nucleic acid supplements, in the form of RNA, can be taken under a physician's supervision.

Susceptibility to Temperature Extremes

Another interesting effect of nucleic acid therapy is that it helps develop resistance to extremes of temperature. The production of ATP (adenasine triphosphate), which is the energy molecule in the cell and which fuels almost all the body's metabolic reactions, is kept in high gear by the intake of nucleic acid. Nucleic acid in the diet helps produce more ATP. This extra energy aids the body in its resistance to extreme cold or heat. Imagine being able to walk outdoors on a cold winter day without hunching up your shoulders and tensing your body against the cold. It is conceivable that this could be the cause of many aches and pains we experience in the winter, hampering our circulation and causing muscular and skeletal discomfort.

Gout

People with gout should follow this diet only under the supervision of a physician.

High Cholesterol and Heart Disease

In most cases arteriosclerosis, which can lead to heart disease and brain damage, is caused by abnormal fat metabolism, often including high blood cholesterol. This thickening of the arteries allows less oxygen-carrying blood to flow, hampering the nourishment of the organs. Nucleic acid helps the heart and brain use smaller amounts of oxygen more efficiently. In addition, nucleic acid-rich diets often lower blood cholesterol. If you have high cholesterol avoid liver, meat, and dairy fats and substitute vegetable oil for butter. Also, limit egg consumption. Once you've been on the diet for a few months it will be safer to include meat occasionally, because the body will be more able to metabolize animal fats. Low-salt or salt-free foods are often advised for those with heart disease or hypertension.

If you have a heart condition, this diet will probably help you. However, it is essential that you continue your medical treatment and allow your physician to adjust your medication as improvement occurs. Do not do it yourself!

A note about the ingredients in the recipes for those concerned about high cholesterol levels or heart disease: When oil is specified, use unhydrogenated vegetable oil; substitute oil for butter. Use a vegetable-oil mayonnaise. Skim milk or noninstant dry milk powder can be substituted for whole milk or cream, or use a combination of skim milk and light cream. Yogurt may be substituted for sour cream; low-fat cheeses may be substituted for other cheeses.

Very few of our recipes call for eggs. However, where eggs are used, the quantity may be reduced if your doctor requires that you limit them. For example, if two eggs are called for in the recipe, use just one. The exception to this would be the use of eggs in a loaf, such as salmon loaf, which requires two eggs; using one egg would affect the consistency and would not work too well. On the other hand, the loaf with two eggs feeds four to six people, so the amount of egg per person is negligible. If you want to use half an egg, beat a whole egg and save half in a closed jar in the refrigerator, where it will keep for a few days.

GLOSSARY OF SPECIAL INGREDIENTS

1. *Agar-agar*—a natural gelatin made from seaweed.
2. *Arrowroot*—a natural vegetable-based thickener.
3. *Miso*—a paste made from fermented soybeans, water, salt, and wheat. Highly nutritious and beneficial to digestive processes.
4. *Soy milk powder*—a high protein, non-dairy powder made from soybeans. It may be used to replace milk as a beverage or in cooking and baking.
5. *Tahini*—a paste made from crushed sesame seeds.
6. *Tamari soy sauce*—aged by natural fermentation of soybeans, water, and salt, with no sugar or chemicals added.
7. *Tofu*—soybean curd, which is highly concentrated protein. Tofu may be used diced in salads, soups, or vegetable dishes, as well as fried for a side dish. It may also be blended in sauces or dressings.
8. *Wakame seaweed*—an Oriental seaweed, packaged in dried strips. It should be washed thoroughly, cut into one inch pieces, and soaked for 15 to 30 minutes, then drained before adding to recipes.

All of the above items may be purchased in health food, Oriental, or Middle Eastern stores.

Part Two

Recipes

SARDINE AND GRILLED CHEESE SANDWICH

whole wheat muffin or bread
butter for spreading
1 3¾-ounce can sardines, drained
Swiss or Jarlsberg cheese

1. Toast muffin or bread and spread with butter.
2. Place sardines on bread and cover with cheese.
3. Put under broiler until cheese bubbles.

SERVES 1

SARDINE-CUCUMBER SPREAD

1 3-ounce package cream cheese
1 tablespoon yogurt
1 teaspoon lemon juice
1 clove garlic, crushed
dash Worcestershire sauce
1 scallion, chopped fine
1 3¾-ounce can sardines or mackerel fillets,
    drained and mashed
1 small cucumber, chopped fine
1 small can black olives, chopped

1. Blend cream cheese, yogurt, lemon juice,
and garlic.
2. Add remaining ingredients and mix well.
3. Chill about 1 hour.
Spread on toast wedges or use for sandwiches.

SERVES 2–4

HOT SARDINE ROLLS

2 3¾-ounce cans sardines, drained
1 tablespoon oil from sardines
1½ tablespoons lemon juice
2 tablespoons finely chopped onion
½ teaspoon white horseradish
8 slices whole wheat bread, crusts removed
2–4 tablespoons melted butter

1. Preheat oven to 400°.

2. Mash sardines and combine with oil, lemon juice, onion, and horseradish.

3. Spread bread slices with mixture.

4. Roll each slice and fasten with a toothpick.

5. Brush top with melted butter and cut rolls in half.

6. Place in shallow pan and bake about 10 minutes at 400° or until rolls are lightly browned.

SERVES 8

SARDINE GUACAMOLE

1 avocado
1 3¾-ounce can well-drained sardines
1 medium tomato, peeled and chopped
    (blanch tomato for easier peeling)
1 small onion or 2 scallions, chopped fine
1 clove garlic, crushed
juice of ½ lemon
pinch chili powder
salt and pepper to taste

Mash avocado and sardines well. Combine with the rest of the ingredients. Chill.

Serve as a dip or on crackers.

SERVES 4

BROILED DEVILED SARDINES

2 tablespoons prepared mustard or 1 tablespoon mustard powder
juice of 1 lemon
1 3¾-ounce can sardines, drained (reserve oil)
3 tablespoons bread crumbs
5 slices whole wheat toast

1. Mix mustard, lemon juice, and reserved oil.

2. Roll sardines in mixture and then in bread crumbs.

3. Broil in shallow pan for 5 minutes.

4. Cut toast into wedges the size of sardines and place a sardine on each wedge. Serve hot.

SERVES 4–6

DEVILED SARDINE SPREAD

1 3¾-ounce can sardines, drained
2 tablespoons prepared mustard or 1 table-
     spoon mustard powder
juice of 1 lemon
5 slices whole wheat toast

1. Mash sardines and combine with mustard
and lemon juice.

2. Cut toast into bite-sized wedges and spread
with sardine mixture.

NOTE: Delicious as a stuffing for celery or tomatoes.

SERVES 4–6

SARDINE AND EGG CANAPÉ

4 hard-cooked eggs
1 3¾-ounce can sardines, drained
3 tablespoons chopped onion
1 teaspoon mustard
1 teaspoon mayonnaise
1 tablespoon chopped fresh parsley

1. Mash egg yolks and sardines.
2. Chop egg whites.
3. Mix with onion, mustard, mayonnaise, and parsley.

Serve on toast strips or crackers.

SERVES 4–6

CURRIED STUFFED EGGS

6 hard-cooked eggs, cut in half
1 3¾-ounce can sardines or salmon, drained
2 tablespoons mayonnaise
2 tablespoons curry powder
dash black pepper

1. Remove egg yolks and mash with sardines or salmon. Add other ingredients.
2. Stuff egg-white halves and chill.
3. Use remaining mixture as a spread.

Serve on lettuce or spinach leaves.

SERVES 4–6

STUFFED CELERY

12–15 stalks celery
1 3¾-ounce can sardines, drained
1 3-ounce package cream cheese
1 tablespoon white horseradish
1 tablespoon grated onion

1. Remove leaves from celery stalks. Chop leaves.

2. Mash sardines and combine with cream cheese, horseradish, onion, and chopped celery leaves.

3. Stuff celery stalks with mixture.

NOTE: This may be used as a spread for crackers.

SERVES 8–12

SALMON SPREAD

1 15½-ounce can salmon
1 hard-cooked egg, mashed
2 tablespoons sesame seeds, toasted
2 tablespoons chopped pimiento or red pepper
2 tablespoons olive oil
juice of ½ lemon
pepper to taste

Mash all ingredients and use as sandwich
spread or for canapes.

NOTE: Fresh salmon, steamed, may be used.

SERVES 4–6

PICKLED SALMON

3 onions, sliced
3 tablespoons mixed pickling spice
5 cups water
3 pounds fresh salmon
½ cup cider vinegar

1. Simmer 2 onions and spice in 2½ cups of water until onions are transparent.

2. Place fish in pan; strain liquid and pour over fish.

3. Add remaining water and vinegar, bring to a boil, and simmer over low heat until cooked yet firm.

4. Place in bowl with remaining raw onion slices; refrigerate overnight.

SERVES 6–8

MUSHROOM-NUT SPREAD

2 onions, chopped fine
1 clove garlic, minced
3 tablespoons oil
1 pound mushrooms, sliced
salt and pepper to taste (optional)
pinch thyme
2 tablespoons chopped walnuts

1. Sauté onions and garlic in oil until golden, add mushrooms, seasoning, and nuts, and sauté until mushrooms are tender.

2. Place mushroom-onion mixture in blender and blend until smooth.

Serve as a canapé or sandwich spread.

SERVES 4–6

MUSHROOM PATÉ

2 onions, chopped
½ pound shallots, chopped
1 leek, sliced
2 cloves garlic, minced
¼ pound butter
2 tablespoons oil
1 pound mushrooms, sliced
pinch each of coriander, cardamom, and pepper
½ teaspoon curry powder
salt to taste
1 bunch fresh dill, chopped

1. Sauté onions, shallots, leek, and garlic in
half the butter and oil until golden.
2. Add mushrooms, remaining butter and oil,
and all seasonings except dill.
3. Cook covered over low heat until mushrooms are tender.
4. Place in blender or food mill and puree until
smooth.
5. Top with dill and chill before serving.
May be used for canapés or as a sandwich
spread.

SERVES 10 as appetizer; 4 sandwiches

STUFFED BROILED MUSHROOMS

1 pound mushrooms (large mushrooms work best for this recipe)
1 4-ounce can chopped clams, drained (reserve broth)
2 tablespoons bread crumbs
1 tablespoon chopped fresh dill or parsley
grated cheese (Cheddar, Parmesan, Swiss)

1. Remove stems from mushrooms. Chop stems.

2. Combine clams, bread crumbs, dill or parsley, mushroom stems, and enough clam broth for a moist consistency.

3. Stuff mushroom caps with mixture and sprinkle cheese on top.

4. Place under broiler for 15 minutes.

SERVES 4–6

BAKED MUSHROOM RISOTTO

1 pound mushrooms (large mushrooms work
   best for this recipe)
3 scallions, chopped
1 clove garlic, crushed
2 tablespoons vegetable oil
1½ cups cooked brown rice
1 teaspoon dried dill weed
pinch oregano
salt and pepper

1. Preheat oven to 350°.

2. Remove stems from mushrooms. Chop stems.

3. Sauté mushroom stems, scallions, and garlic in oil.

4. Combine with the rice and add remaining ingredients.

5. Stuff mushroom caps with mixture and bake covered at 350° for about 20 minutes.

May be served hot or cold.

SERVES 4–6

RUSSIAN LOBIO DIP

6 cups red kidney beans, cooked
2 onions, chopped
2 tablespoons oil
3−4 cloves garlic, crushed
dash coriander
3 sprigs fresh dill, chopped
¼−½ pound shelled walnuts, chopped
salt and pepper to taste

1. Mash or blend beans.
2. Sauté onions in oil until lightly browned.
Add to beans with the oil.
3. Stir in remaining ingredients.
Use as a dip with raw vegetables or corn chips.

MAKES 5 CUPS

MACKEREL PATTIES

1 4⅜-ounce can mackerel fillets
1 egg, beaten
1 onion, diced
1 potato, mashed
salt and pepper to taste

1. Mix all ingredients.
2. Make patties and broil until lightly browned on both sides.

NOTE: If ingredients are doubled, this is a delicious main course.

SERVES 4

HUMUS

1 can chick peas, drained (reserve water)
4 tablespoons tahini
2 cloves garlic, crushed
juice of 2 lemons
2 tablespoons olive oil
salt and pepper to taste
2 tablespoons chopped parsley

1. Place all ingredients except parsley in blender. Process until smooth.
2. Add enough liquid from chick peas for desired consistency.
3. Remove from blender and stir in parsley.

SERVES 4–6

ASPARAGUS DIP OR SPREAD

½ pound asparagus, steamed
½ cup French dressing (see Dressings)
¼ pound sharp Cheddar cheese, cubed or
  grated

Place all ingredients in blender. Process until smooth.

SERVES 4

VEGETABLE STOCK

1 large onion, sliced, with peel
2 stalks celery, sliced, with leaves
2 carrots, sliced, with greens
¼ head cabbage, chopped
2 tablespoons oil
potato peelings (optional)
2 quarts water, boiling
1 turnip or parsnip, sliced
½ bunch parsley, chopped
1 bay leaf
salt and pepper to taste

1. Sauté onion, celery, carrots, and cabbage in oil lightly.
2. Add 2 quarts boiling water and remaining ingredients.
3. Simmer 2 hours or until vegetables are thoroughly cooked.
4. Strain and serve.

NOTE: Recipe may be doubled and stored in refrigerator for a week or in freezer for a month.

SERVES 4–6

ITALIAN LENTIL SOUP

1 cup lentils, washed and picked over
4 tomatoes, peeled (blanch tomato for
    easier peeling)
4–5 cups water or stock
1 onion, diced
2 cloves garlic, crushed
dash each of oregano, basil, and cayenne
    pepper
1 tablespoon oil
1 tablespoon cream (optional)

1. Cook lentils and tomatoes in water or stock until lentils are soft—about 45 minutes.

2. Meanwhile, sauté onion, garlic, and seasonings in oil until onions are golden.

3. Place mixture in blender and process until smooth.

4. Add cream and heat through.

SERVES 4–6

EASY LENTIL-NOODLE SOUP

1 cup lentils, washed and picked over, soaked
    4 hours
¼ pound whole wheat noodles or macaroni
4 cups water, boiling
1 clove garlic, crushed
2 tablespoons oil
1 teaspoon thyme
salt and pepper to taste

1. Drain lentils and add with noodles to boiling
water. Return water to boil.

2. Meanwhile, sauté garlic in oil until brown;
add seasonings and add to soup.

3. Simmer over low heat until lentils and noodles are tender.

Serve hot.

SERVES 4−6

MOROCCAN
LENTIL SOUP

1½ cups lentils, washed and picked over
3 cups water
juice of 1 lemon
1 pound small onions, whole
¼ cup plus 2 tablespoons oil
4 threads saffron, dissolved in small amount of
   water
2 pounds tomatoes, peeled and cut in chunks
   (blanch tomatoes for easier peeling)
2½ quarts water
4 tablespoons whole wheat flour
½ cup lemon juice
1 bunch parsley, chopped
1 tablespoon coriander
salt to taste

1. Cook lentils in 3 cups water until tender.
Drain water, mash lentils, and add juice of 1
lemon.

2. Meanwhile, cook onions, ¼ cup oil, and saffron in enough water to cover for about 1 hour.

3. Cook tomatoes in 2½ quarts water and 2
tablespoons oil for 15 minutes.

4. Dilute flour in small amount of liquid, add
additional lemon juice, and then add to soup.
Cook until thickened.

5. Add seasonings, onion mixture, and lentils
and heat thoroughly.

NOTE: Chick peas may be substituted for lentils.

SERVES 8–10

LENTIL AND BROWN RICE SOUP

½ cup brown rice
1 cup brown lentils, washed and picked over
1½ quarts water or broth
2 carrots, sliced
2 celery stalks with leaves, sliced
2 medium-size onions, diced
2 cloves garlic, crushed
2 tablespoons oil
1 bay leaf
1 tablespoon fresh chopped dill or 1 teaspoon
  dried dill weed
salt and pepper to taste
dash lemon juice
dash tamari soy sauce

1. Place rice and lentils in cold water or broth, bring to a boil, and simmer for 40 minutes.

2. Sauté vegetables in oil.

3. Puree cooked rice and lentils in blender or food mill.

4. Combine rice and lentils with vegetables and seasonings; simmer for 30 minutes; add lemon juice and tamari soy sauce just before serving.

Add additional broth or water if soup is too thick.

SERVES 6–8

DAL SOUP

Follow recipe for dal (page 130). Use vegetable stock instead of water and increase quantity to 1½ quarts.

Follow procedure through step 4 and add remaining stock. Bring to a boil, cover, and simmer for 10 minutes. A dash of lemon juice and curry powder to taste may be added just before serving.

SERVES 4–6

LENTIL–SWEET POTATO SOUP

1 cup lentils, washed and picked over
4 cups water
1 large sweet potato, sliced
salt and pepper to taste
pinch of rosemary or marjoram
handful of spinach, chopped

1. Boil lentils in water until soft—about 45 minutes.

2. Put through food mill or blender.

3. Return to pot and add sweet potato slices and seasonings.

4. Cook until potatoes are tender.

5. Add spinach, stir, remove from heat and serve.

SERVES 4–5

OATMEAL SOUP

1 onion, chopped fine
1 tablespoon oil
1 cup rolled oats
salt and pepper to taste
4 cups water or stock
2 cups milk
3 tablespoons chopped parsley

1. Sauté onion in oil until golden.

2. Add oats and seasoning, stir, and brown lightly.

3. Add stock, stirring continually, and bring to a boil.

4. Simmer covered for about 45 minutes.

5. Remove from heat, let stand uncovered until slightly cooled; add milk and reheat, if necessary. Garnish with parsley.

SERVES 4–6

BORSCHT I

1 pound beets, with leaves
1 quart water
2 tablespoons honey
juice of ½ lemon
dollop sour cream or yogurt

1. Remove stems from beets and scrub beets well; reserve leaves.

2. Boil beets in water until tender.

3. Remove beets, cut leaves in small pieces, and add to liquid. Simmer 10 minutes.

4. Add honey and stir well until dissolved.

5. Chill soup and beets. When thoroughly chilled peel beets and grate into soup. Add lemon juice and serve with sour cream or yogurt.

SERVES 4

BORSCHT II

1 pound beets, chopped fine or grated
1½ quarts vegetable stock or water
juice of 1 lemon
1 egg yolk, beaten
1 tablespoon yogurt or sour cream
1 teaspoon fresh chopped dill
salt and pepper to taste
4 medium potatoes, boiled and sliced

1. Boil beets in stock or water until soft.

2. Combine lemon juice, egg yolk, yogurt, and seasonings and set aside.

3. Remove soup from heat and allow to cool.

4. Beat yogurt mixture into soup and serve with slices of boiled potatoes.

NOTE: May be served hot or cold. Beets may be pureed if desired.

SERVES 4–6

CREAM OF ASPARAGUS SOUP

¾ pound fresh asparagus, cut in small pieces
1 tablespoon oil
1 quart vegetable stock or water
½ teaspoon salt
2 cups cream or milk
pinch each sage and rosemary
pepper to taste

1. Sauté asparagus lightly in oil.

2. Add stock and salt; bring to a boil.

3. Simmer over low heat until asparagus is well cooked—about ½ hour.

4. Add cream or milk and other seasonings, mix well, and remove from heat.

NOTE: Cauliflower, mushrooms, spinach, or broccoli may be used instead of asparagus. Soup may be pureed before cream is added.

SERVES 4–6

RADISH GREENS SOUP

1 small onion, chopped
1 tablespoon oil
1½ quarts vegetable stock
½ teaspoon salt
½ pound radish greens, chopped
2 tablespoons miso paste
1 teaspoon basil

1. Sauté onion in oil.

2. Add stock and bring to a boil.

3. Add salt and greens. Simmer 10 minutes.

4. Dilute miso paste in 4 tablespoons of hot stock, remove soup from heat, and add miso and basil to soup.

Allow to stand about 5 minutes before serving.

NOTE: Spinach or chard may be used instead of radish greens.

SERVES 6

FISH STOCK

2 pounds fish (a variety may be used)
2½ quarts water
1 onion, sliced
3–4 cloves garlic, chopped
½ cup oil
½ bunch parsley, chopped
1 bay leaf
4–5 peppercorns
¾ cup white wine
4–5 tomatoes, quartered
salt to taste

1. Place fish in water. When about to boil add onion, garlic, oil, parsley, bay leaf, and peppercorns.

2. When water boils add wine, tomatoes, and salt.

3. Simmer covered for 20 minutes; remove fish and strain soup.

May be served unstrained as a soup with rice or used as stock.

NOTE: Fish may be used for salad. Quantity may be increased and stored in freezer.

SERVES 8

RITA'S NEW ENGLAND CLAM CHOWDER

2 onions, minced
2 tablespoons butter
1 dozen fresh clams, opened and chopped (reserve liquid)
1 10½-ounce can minced clams (reserve liquid)
2 medium potatoes, cubed
3 cups milk (or 1½ cups skim milk and 1½ cups whole milk)
2 teaspoons arrowroot, dissolved in ½ cup cold water
dash cayenne pepper
salt to taste

1. Sauté onions in butter until golden.

2. Add clam broth reserved from fresh and canned clams.

3. Add potatoes. Simmer until potatoes are tender but firm—about 15 minutes.

4. Add milk and stir in arrowroot.

5. Simmer until thickened (do not boil).

6. Add fresh and canned clams. Add salt and pepper; simmer for a few minutes. (Prolonged cooking will toughen the clams.)

SERVES 4

SPLIT PEA SOUP

1 large onion, chopped
2 stalks celery, chopped
1 carrot, chopped
2 cloves garlic, crushed
2 tablespoons oil or butter
1½ quarts vegetable stock
1 cup split peas, rinsed
salt and pepper to taste

1. Sauté onion, celery, carrot, and garlic in oil or butter.

2. Add stock; bring to a boil.

3. Add peas and seasoning. Lower heat and simmer for about 2 hours or until peas are very soft.

NOTE: You may add a dash of lemon juice before serving.

SERVES 4–6

MINESTRONE

1 onion, chopped
1 clove garlic, minced
1 tablespoon olive oil
6 cups stock
1 carrot, cubed
2 tomatoes, cubed
1 stalk celery
pinch each parsley, oregano, and basil
salt and pepper to taste
½ cup cooked chick peas
½ cup whole wheat elbow macaroni
grated Parmesan cheese

1. Sauté onion and garlic in oil until golden.
2. Add stock and bring to a boil.
3. Add vegetables and seasonings; simmer until tender.
4. Meanwhile, parboil macaroni.
5. Add macaroni and chick peas to the soup; simmer 10 to 15 minutes.

Serve with grated cheese.

SERVES 4–5

SPROUT SOUP

1½ quarts vegetable stock
½ cup soybean sprouts
½ cup mung bean sprouts
dash tamari soy sauce
½ teaspoon fresh grated ginger

1. Bring stock to a boil.

2. Add sprouts and simmer 5 minutes.

3. Add tamari soy sauce and ginger and re-move from heat.

SERVES 4–6

MUSHROOM-BARLEY SOUP

1 onion, chopped
1 clove garlic, minced
1 cup barley
2 tablespoons oil or butter
½ pound mushrooms, sliced
6 cups stock
1 bunch parsley, chopped fine
pinch each nutmeg and thyme
½ teaspoon grated fresh ginger
salt and pepper to taste

1. Sauté onions, garlic, and barley in oil or butter until golden brown.

2. Add mushrooms and sauté lightly.

3. Add stock; bring to a boil.

4. Add seasonings, cover, and simmer for about 1 hour.

NOTE: Dried mushrooms may be used. Soak for about 1 hour prior to cooking.

SERVES 6

CLEAR SOUP
WITH SPINACH

1 large onion with skin, cut in quarters
1 carrot, cut in chunks
2 celery stalks with leaves, cut in large pieces
½ bunch parsley, chopped
1 parsnip, cut in pieces
2 strips wakame seaweed (optional)
1 teaspoon salt
1 bay leaf
3 tablespoons fresh dill, chopped
1½ quarts water
1 clove garlic, minced
1 whole clove
½ teaspoon nutmeg
pinch white pepper
¼ pound spinach, rinsed well, chopped with
   stalks
2 tablespoons tamari soy sauce (optional)

1. Boil vegetables, salt, bay leaf, and dill in water until vegetables are cooked.

2. Add remaining ingredients except spinach and tamari, stir well; cook additional 10 minutes.

3. Strain soup through cheesecloth, add spinach, and reheat until spinach is slightly wilted. Add tamari.

NOTE: Chopped scallions or sprouts can be added at the same time as spinach.

SERVES 6–8

MISO SOUP

1 onion, sliced thin
1 carrot, sliced thin
¼ head cabbage, sliced thin
2 tablespoons oil
3 strips wakame seaweed, washed and soaked
    (optional)
5 cups water or vegetable stock, boiling
½ pound Japanese whole wheat noodles
    (soba)
2 tablespoons miso paste, diluted in ½ cup
    water
2 squares tofu (soybean curd)

1. Sauté vegetables in oil.

2. Add boiling water or stock and seaweed;
simmer until vegetables are tender—about 15
minutes.

3. Meanwhile, boil noodles for 5 minutes.

4. Add miso and mix well. Add tofu, remove
from heat, and add noodles.

SERVES 4–6

BLACK BEAN SOUP

1 cup dry black beans, cooked (reserve liquid)
1 large onion, diced
1 stalk celery, chopped, with leaves
2 cloves garlic, minced
⅔ cup raw brown rice
¼ cup oil
6 cups stock (bean liquid and/or vegetable stock)
pinch cayenne pepper
1 bay leaf
½ teaspoon dry mustard
1½ teaspoons salt
dash pepper
2 whole cloves
dash lemon juice or cider vinegar

1. Drain beans when tender and mash slightly.
2. Sauté onion, celery, garlic, and rice in oil until onion is golden.
3. Stir in stock and add beans and seasonings.
4. Simmer covered over low heat for about 1 hour.
5. Add lemon juice or vinegar just before serving.

SERVES 6

SARDINE-POTATO SALAD

8 medium-sized potatoes, boiled in skins,
   peeled and warm
1 3¾-ounce can sardines, packed in olive oil
4 tablespoons olive oil
2 tablespoons lemon juice
⅛ teaspoon dry mustard
¼ – ½ teaspoon salt
¼ teaspoon pepper
3 sprigs fresh parsley, chopped fine
1 teaspoon fresh chives, chopped fine
1 head romaine lettuce
2 stalks celery, chopped fine
1 cucumber, sliced thin
2 hard-cooked eggs, peeled and quartered

1. Slice warm potatoes into mixing bowl.

2. Drain oil from sardines into separate bowl,
set sardines aside, and add olive oil to sardine oil.

3. Using a wire whisk, add to oil: lemon juice,
mustard, salt, pepper, parsley, and chives;
blend well, pour over potatoes, and toss lightly.

4. When potatoes are cool, line salad bowl with
lettuce.

5. Add the sardines, celery, and cucumber
slices to potatoes, toss lightly, spoon into salad
bowl.

6. Top with egg quarters.

May be served chilled or at room temperature.

SERVES 6–8

SARDINE NICOISE

1   3¾-ounce can sardines, drained
1   head lettuce
2   tomatoes, cut in quarters
2   large potatoes, boiled and cut in cubes
1   small can black olives
4   hard-cooked eggs, sliced or quartered
1   medium-size red onion, cut in thin rings

Place all ingredients on a bed of lettuce leaves in a decorative fashion.

Serve French Dressing (see Dressings) on the side.

SERVES 4 – 6

LUNCHEON SALAD

1 head romaine lettuce or ½ pound spinach,
   washed and torn
1 carrot, thinly sliced
1 stalk celery, sliced
2 scallions, sliced
½ pound mushrooms, sliced
2 cans mackerel fillets
French dressing (see Dressings)

Place all ingredients in a bowl and toss lightly;
add French dressing just before serving.

NOTE: Any leftover cold vegetables and/or beans
may be added. Tofu (soybean curd) may be
used instead of mackerel fillets.

SERVES 4–6

SHRIMP SALAD

1 pound cold shrimp, cut in small pieces
1 small onion, minced fine
2 tablespoons yogurt
2 tablespoons mayonnaise
salt and pepper to taste
1 tablespoon fresh dill, chopped fine
pinch mustard powder
2 or 3 avocados, halved and pitted, or romaine
    lettuce leaves

Combine all ingredients except avocados or lettuce.

Serve in avocado halves or on a bed of lettuce leaves.

SERVES 4−6

TABOULI
WITH LENTILS

1 cup bulgur wheat
2 cups hot water
½ bunch parsley, chopped fine
2 scallions, chopped fine
2 tablespoons chopped fresh mint
1 tomato, chopped
½–¾ cup cooked lentils
juice of 1 lemon
½ cup oil
salt and pepper to taste
lettuce leaves

1. Soak bulgur in hot water until water is absorbed.
2. Combine with remaining ingredients and chill thoroughly.

Serve on lettuce leaves.

SERVES 4–6

CHICK PEA
SALAD

2 cups cooked chick peas
2 tomatoes, cubed
8 radishes, sliced
½ red onion, diced
handful alfalfa sprouts

Combine all ingredients.
Serve with tahini dressing or tomato-garlic
dressing (see Dressings).

SERVES 4–6

LENTIL-RICE
SALAD

1 cup cooked lentils
1–1½ cups cooked brown rice
4 tablespoons olive oil or vegetable oil
2 scallions, cut in small pieces
pinch turmeric
2 tablespoons lemon juice

Combine all ingredients.
Serve chilled.

SERVES 4–6

BLUEBERRY-RICE SALAD

2 cups cooked brown rice, cold
2 cups fresh blueberries
½ cup almonds, chopped
honey to taste
½ cup soy milk powder
salt to taste
⅔ cup oil
2 tablespoons lemon juice

1. Combine rice, berries, almonds, and honey.

2. Blend soy milk powder, salt, and a little honey; add oil slowly, blending until thick. Stir in lemon juice.

3. Mix the rice mixture with the soy milk mixture.

SERVES 4–6

BEAN SALAD

1 16-ounce can black beans, black-eyed peas,
   or chick peas (cooked dried beans may be
   used)
1 small onion, minced fine
2 tablespoons olive oil
1 tablespoon cider vinegar
salt and pepper to taste

Mix all ingredients.
Serve hot or cold, with brown rice.

SERVES 4–6

PICKLED VEGETABLES

1 cup olive oil
¾ cup cider vinegar
4 cloves garlic, crushed
salt and pepper to taste
1 tablespoon honey (optional)
1 head cauliflower, broken into flowerets
1 turnip, sliced
2 green peppers, sliced
2 asparagus stalks
½ pound mushrooms, sliced
6 small white onions
10 Greek olives

1. Bring oil, vinegar, garlic, salt, pepper, and honey to a boil and cook for 5 minutes.
2. Allow liquid to cool for 5 minutes. Snap off tough ends of asparagus stalks. Pour liquid over vegetables.
3. Cover and refrigerate for at least a day.
4. Restore to room temperature before serving.

SERVES 6–8

ASPARAGUS VINAIGRETTE

1 pound asparagus
¾ cup olive oil
⅓ cup cider vinegar
½ teaspoon mustard powder
1 clove garlic, crushed
2 teaspoons toasted sesame seeds
salt and pepper to taste
romaine lettuce or raw spinach leaves

1. Snap off tough ends of asparagus stalks.
Steam asparagus until tender but firm, and
allow to cool.

2. Combine remaining ingredients and pour
over asparagus.

3. Chill thoroughly.

Serve on bed of lettuce or spinach leaves.

SERVES 4

MARINATED RAW BEET SALAD

1 pound beets, peeled, tops removed,
   scrubbed well and grated
2 onions, thinly sliced

Marinade:
½ cup olive oil
juice of 2 lemons
salt and pepper to taste
1 tablespoon fresh dill, chopped
romaine lettuce or raw spinach leaves (optional)

1. Mix together all marinade ingredients. Put
beets and onions in marinade for 1 hour or
more.

2. Drain excess marinade.

3. Serve on lettuce or spinach leaves, or use as
a relish.

SERVES 4–6

SPINACH-STUFFED TOMATOES

4 large tomatoes
salt to taste
½ pound spinach, chopped fine and pounded
2 tablespoons olive oil
4 cloves garlic, crushed
romaine lettuce leaves

1. Cut tops off tomatoes and scoop out insides; salt insides and turn shell upside down to drain.
2. Combine spinach, tomato pulp, olive oil, and garlic.
3. Divide mixture into 4 equal parts and fill each tomato; refrigerate 1 hour.
Serve chilled on lettuce leaves.

SERVES 4

MUSHROOM-SPINACH SALAD

1 pound spinach, torn
1 pound mushrooms, sliced
1 red onion, sliced thin
1 cup cooked chick peas
1 cup French dressing (see Dressings)
2 hard-cooked eggs, chopped

Combine all ingredients except eggs, add dressing, and toss; sprinkle chopped eggs on top.

SERVES 4–6

SPINACH-BEET SALAD

1 pound spinach or escarole, washed and torn
4 small beets, washed, peeled, and grated
     (cooked beets may be used)
French or tahini dressing (see Dressings)
2 hard-cooked eggs, chopped
½ cup pumpkin or sunflower seeds
whole wheat croutons

1. Combine spinach and beets.
2. Toss lightly with dressing.
3. Sprinkle with eggs, seeds, and croutons.

SERVES 4–6

CAESAR SALAD

1 head romaine lettuce, torn
2 scallions, chopped
2 tomatoes, cut in wedges
1 can black olives
1 can anchovies, drained
grated Parmesan cheese, to taste
1 cup whole wheat croutons
½ cup French dressing (see Dressings) mixed
   with one egg yolk

Combine all ingredients and toss lightly with
dressing.

SERVES 6–8

Dressings and Sauces

BEET OR SPINACH MAYONNAISE

½ pound beets, cooked until tender *or*
   ½ pound spinach, torn and steamed lightly
1 cup mayonnaise

1. Puree beets or spinach in blender.
2. Add mayonnaise gradually.

Serve over salad, hot or cold vegetables, or fish.

NOTE: This mayonnaise may also be put in a
pastry bag and used to decorate salad, vegetables, or fish dishes. The dressing will be pink or
green.

BREWER'S YEAST DRESSING

2 cups olive oil
juice of 3 lemons
2 cloves garlic, chopped
1 teaspoon tamari soy sauce
½ teaspoon curry powder
1 egg yolk
1 tablespoon brewer's yeast (mild flavor)
salt and pepper to taste

Place all ingredients in blender and process until smooth; may be stored in refrigerator.

May be used on salads or cooked vegetables.

NOTE: There are many varieties of brewer's yeast. Use the debittered, mildest-tasting kind available.

MAKES 1 QUART

FRENCH DRESSING

¼ cup olive oil
juice of 1 lemon
1 clove garlic, crushed
pinch mustard powder
dash tamari soy sauce
salt and pepper to taste

Combine all ingredients and blend well.

MAKES ⅓ CUP

ANCHOVY GREEN DRESSING

1 cup yogurt
¼ pound spinach, chopped
1 can anchovies, drained
1 clove garlic, chopped
pepper to taste

Blend all ingredients until smooth; chill and
serve over salad, hot or cold vegetables, or
grains.

MAKES 2 CUPS

TAHINI DRESSING

½ cup cold water
3 tablespoons tahini
juice of 1 lemon
1 clove garlic, minced
2 tablespoons yogurt (optional)
salt and pepper to taste

Combine all ingredients and blend. Serve over salad or raw or cooked vegetables.

MAKES 1 CUP

TOMATO-GARLIC DRESSING

1 egg yolk
3 ripe tomatoes, quartered
2 cloves garlic, chopped
salt and pepper to taste
2 tablespoons vinegar
½ cup oil

Place all ingredients in blender and process until smooth.

MAKES 2 CUPS

SAUCE CALCUTTA
FOR FISH

1 cup sour cream
¼ cup chutney
1 tablespoon Dijon or English mustard

Mix well and chill. Serve over cold fish or seafood.

GREEN SAUCE
FOR FISH

½ cup French mustard (not powder)
½ cup oil
juice of 1 lemon
1 tablespoon cider vinegar
4 small pickled cucumbers, chopped fine
2 tablespoons chopped onions
3 tablespoons chopped parsley
salt and pepper to taste
anchovy paste to taste

Combine all ingredients and mix well.
Serve over fish.

SERVES 4–6

CLAM SAUCE

1 onion, diced
2 cloves garlic, crushed or minced
1 tablespoon olive oil
2 10½-ounce cans minced clams (reserve
  broth)
1 teaspoon oregano

1. Sauté onion and garlic lightly in oil.

2. Add clam broth and oregano; simmer covered for 5 minutes.

3. Remove from heat and add clams.

Serve over linguine or other pasta.

SERVES 4

ISRAELI YOGURT-CUCUMBER SAUCE

1 cup yogurt
1 egg yolk, beaten (optional)
1 clove garlic, crushed
1 teaspoon lemon juice
½ teaspoon mustard powder
pinch cayenne pepper
salt to taste
1 cucumber, diced

1. Combine yogurt, egg yolk, garlic, lemon juice, mustard powder, cayenne, and salt; mix well.

2. Place over low heat but do not allow to boil. Stir constantly.

3. Add cucumber and heat through.

Serve hot over fish, vegetables, or grains.

NOTE: May be poured over fish before baking.

MAKES 1½ CUPS

SARDINE PESTO SAUCE ITALIEN

½ pound spinach, chopped
½ pound fresh basil, chopped
1 cup olive oil
3 cloves garlic, chopped
⅛ cup Parmesan cheese, grated
⅛ cup Romano cheese, grated
1 3¾-ounce can sardines with oil
½ cup pignoli (pine nuts) or walnuts
2 tablespoons heavy cream

Place all ingredients in blender except cream.
Blend until smooth, then stir in cream.

Serve over pasta or rice.

SERVES 4–6

SARDINE-TOMATO SAUCE

1 large onion, diced
2 cloves garlic, crushed
1 tablespoon olive oil
1 large can (stewed or pureed) tomatoes
1 small can tomato paste
pinch each basil and red pepper
salt to taste
2 3¾-ounce cans sardines in oil

1. Sauté onion and garlic in olive oil until golden.
2. Add tomatoes and tomato paste and stir well.
3. Add seasonings and simmer for 1 hour.
4. Mash sardines with oil from can.
5. Remove sauce from heat, add sardines, and stir.
Serve over pasta or rice.

SERVES 4–6

SAUCE VEGETARIAN

1 onion, chopped
1 clove garlic, minced
1 stalk celery, chopped with leaves
1 tomato, chopped
1 carrot, sliced
2 tablespoons oil
pinch each basil and thyme
salt and pepper to taste
vegetable stock
dash tamari soy sauce

1. Sauté all vegetables lightly in oil.

2. Add seasonings.

3. Place in blender with enough stock to liquefy and add tamari.

4. Blend until smooth. Reheat.

Serve over grains or fish.

MAKES 2 CUPS

MIDDLE EAST
TAHINI SAUCE

1 large onion, chopped
2 tablespoons sesame oil
2 tablespoons tahini
½ cup cold water
arrowroot or whole wheat flour
1 tablespoon tamari soy sauce

1. Sauté onion in oil until golden.

2. Mix in tahini and water, stirring constantly.

3. Add just enough arrowroot or flour to thicken slightly—about 1 teaspoon.

4. Remove from heat and add tamari.

Serve over fish, vegetables, or grains.

MAKES 1 CUP

Main Courses

FISH AND SEAFOOD

Tips on Buying and Cooking Fish

It is important to use fish that is fresh. Whenever possible, take advantage of locally caught fish. It's not only freshest but least expensive. Even fresh fish must be bought with a careful eye and nose (the fish store may have just received a catch which was out at sea for several weeks).

Look for bright, clear, upturned eyes; firm flesh (particularly around the bone) which will not remain dented when pressed; bright skin color (or white in fish like halibut); blood showing around the gills and bones; and no strong "fishy" smell. This last is most important—smell is usually the clearest indication that a fish is spoiling and losing nutritional value.

Sometimes the storekeeper will try to pass off a fish as fresh which has been frozen. Defrosted fish can be detected by a collapsed look of the body and a wilted tail. It will be dried out and will break easily. It is easier to determine freshness in whole fish than in fillets, so if possible buy a whole fish and have it filleted for you (soups and court bouillon can be made from the heads and bones). The whole fish is often as economical as fillets.

If you must buy frozen fish, make sure that it is frozen solid and rewrap it before placing it in the refrigerator or freezer. If there is any discoloration or fishy smell, be suspicious. Defrost fish as slowly as possible, preferably in the refrigerator for twenty-four hours, and dry it thoroughly. If you are in a hurry you can cook fish while it is frozen, but drain it well and allow a little more cooking time.

Many fish are interchangeable in recipes. Generally, fatty fish are best for broiling and baking and lean fish for sautéing, poaching, and soups. When cooking whole fish, allow 1 pound per person.

Fish should never be overcooked. It should be moist and tender—cooked only until it is opaque and flakes easily. Some methods of cooking are baking, poaching in a court bouillon, quick-sautéing (dipped in milk and flour), pan frying, and deep frying in batter (particularly good for whole fish). Garnishes like almonds, lemon wedges, and fresh parsley or dill dress up the fish dish. Broiled or grilled fish is especially good with sauces.

SARDINES LOMBARDY

2 pounds fresh sardines, cleaned and heads re-
    moved
1 cup whole wheat flour
1 teaspoon sage
salt and pepper to taste
½ cup oil
lemon wedges

1. Wash sardines well and pat dry.

2. Combine flour, sage, salt, and pepper; roll
sardines in mixture.

3. Fry slowly in hot oil until browned on both
sides.

Serve with lemon wedges.

SERVES 4

SARDINE QUICHE

Crust:
1−1½ cups oil
2 cups whole wheat pastry flour
1 teaspoon salt
1 cup (approximately) cold water

1. Preheat oven to 425°.
2. Mix oil with flour and salt until crumbly.
3. Add water and mix with hands; mixture should come off bowl easily but should not be wet; do not overmix and handle gently.
4. Form into a ball, place on a floured surface, and roll out dough quickly to size of 9-inch pie pan, with enough dough to overlap edge of pan.
5. Transfer rolled dough to pie plate.
6. Bake crust for about 10 minutes at 425°; allow to cool.

Filling:
1 onion, chopped
1 tablespoon oil
4 eggs, beaten
2 cups milk
1 teaspoon salt
1 teaspoon pepper
½ teaspoon nutmeg
2 3¾-ounce cans sardines (packed in water), drained
½ pound Swiss or Jarlsberg cheese, cut in cubes

1. Preheat oven to 350°.

2. Sauté onions in oil until golden.

3. Place onions on crust.

4. Mix eggs, milk, and seasonings and pour over onions.

5. Distribute sardines and place cheese cubes on top.

6. Bake at 350° for about 40 minutes or until mixture sets.

SERVES 4–6

BAKED PIQUANTE SARDINES

4 scallions, cut in strips
1 onion, sliced thin
2 tablespoons olive oil
2 cloves garlic, crushed
juice of 2 lemons
1 teaspoon ground cumin
pinch saffron
salt and pepper to taste
4 cans sardines, drained
2 tablespoons chopped parsley

1. Preheat oven to 350°.

2. Sauté scallions and onion in oil until golden.

3. Add garlic, lemon juice, and seasonings and simmer 10 minutes.

4. Place drained sardines in bottom of a greased, ovenproof casserole.

5. Pour sauce over sardines and bake for 5 minutes in 350° oven.

6. Garnish with fresh parsley.

SERVES 4–5

SWEET AND SOUR SALMON

2 onions, sliced
2 tablespoons vegetable oil
2 tablespoons whole wheat flour
1 cup vegetable or fish broth
juice of 1½ lemons
¼ cup honey
handful raisins (optional)
salt to taste
4 salmon steaks, ½ inch thick

1. Brown onions in oil and add flour, stirring constantly.

2. Gradually add broth and bring to boil.

3. Add lemon juice, honey, raisins, and salt; mix well.

4. Place salmon steaks on top of mixture; lower heat, cover, and simmer until salmon is cooked (about 15 minutes).

5. Place salmon on platter and cover with sauce.

Serve hot or cold.

SERVES 4

SALMON CUSTARD

2 eggs, beaten
½ cup cream
1 tablespoon chopped chives
½ teaspoon dry mustard
¼ teaspoon dill weed
salt and pepper to taste
1 7¾-ounce can salmon, drained and flaked
dash paprika

1. Preheat oven to 350°.

2. Mix all ingredients (blend if desired).

3. Place in individual greased casseroles or 1 large greased casserole.

4. Set casseroles in shallow pan containing 1 inch of water.

5. Bake at 350° for 30 minutes or until knife inserted in custard comes out clean.

SERVES 4

SALMON STEAK
À LA MODE

1 salmon steak per person
sour cream or yogurt
fresh chopped dill or dried dill weed

1. Preheat oven to 350°.

2. Place salmon on greased baking dish, put a dollop of sour cream or yogurt on each steak, and sprinkle with dill.

3. Bake at 350° for 20–30 minutes, depending on thickness of steaks.

SALMON AND RICE CROQUETTES

3 salmon steaks, ½ inch thick, chopped or 7-
ounce can salmon
3 cups cooked rice
1 tablespoon fresh chopped dill
2 scallions, chopped
½ teaspoon fresh grated ginger
2 tablespoons whole wheat flour or wheat
germ
1 egg, beaten
salt and pepper to taste
oil for frying

1. Combine all ingredients except oil and form
into croquettes.

2. Fry in oil or bake on greased cookie sheet or
shallow pan at 350° until brown on both sides.

3. Serve with tomato or brown sauce, or
yogurt on the side if desired.

SERVES 4–6

POACHED SALMON STEAK

4 salmon steaks, about 1 inch thick
salted water
4 tablespoons melted butter or oil
juice of 1 lemon
2 tablespoons chopped parsley
salt and pepper to taste

1. In large skillet bring about ½ inch salted water to a boil.

2. Place salmon steaks in boiling water, return to boil, cover, simmer for about 10 minutes or until steaks are flaky.

3. Combine melted butter with lemon juice, parsley, salt, and pepper.

4. Gently remove steaks from skillet; cover with sauce.

NOTE: Sauce may be thickened by dissolving 1 tablespoon arrowroot in half the excess water, boiling for a minute or two, and adding to butter sauce.

SERVES 4

EGGPLANT AND SALMON À LA GRECQUE

1 medium eggplant, cut in ½-inch slices
4 salmon steaks, 1 inch thick
2 tablespoons butter
juice of ½ lemon
salt and pepper to taste
½ pound spinach
½ pound feta cheese

1. Preheat oven to 350°.

2. Place eggplant slices in a greased baking dish.

3. Place salmon steaks on top, dot with butter, and sprinkle with lemon juice and seasonings.

4. Bake about 20 minutes.

5. Meanwhile steam spinach until wilted.

6. Remove baking dish from oven; place spinach around salmon and top with feta cheese.

7. Broil until cheese bubbles.

SERVES 4

SALMON LOAF

1 15½-ounce can salmon (reserve juice)
2 eggs, beaten
1 carrot, grated
1 onion, grated
¾ cup wheat germ or bread crumbs, *or* mixture of both
1 tablespoon yogurt or sour cream
1 teaspoon baking powder

1. Preheat oven to 350°.

2. Mix all ingredients except baking powder and juice from salmon.

3. Mix baking powder with reserved salmon juice and fold into mixture.

3. Place in greased loaf pan and bake at 350° for 30–40 minutes.

May be served hot or cold.

SERVES 4

SWEET AND SOUR SHRIMP

1 pound shrimp, cleaned
1 tablespoon honey
2 tablespoons arrowroot dissolved in ¼ cup
   cold water
¼ cup lemon juice
1 tablespoon tamari soy sauce
1 teaspoon fresh grated ginger
2½ cups pineapple chunks (packed in natural
   juice)
1 tomato, peeled and cut in small chunks
1 green pepper, sliced
1 large onion, sliced
1 carrot, sliced thin
salt to taste

1. Cook shrimp in boiling water for 3 minutes.
Drain.

2. Combine honey, arrowroot, lemon juice, tamari, ginger, and small amount of juice from
pineapple and simmer over low heat, stirring
constantly until thickened.

3. Add tomato, green pepper, onion, carrot, and pineapple; simmer 5 minutes.

4. Add shrimp and bring to a boil.

Serve over rice.

SERVES 4–6

SHRIMP OR LOBSTER MOUSSE

1 tablespoon flakes or ¼ bar agar-agar (sea-weed gelatin) Unflavored gelatin may be substituted.
½ cup cold water
¾ cup mayonnaise
2 tablespoons lemon juice
1 stalk celery, chopped
½ onion, chopped
1½ cups cooked shrimp or lobster
salt and pepper to taste
2 tablespoons heavy cream, whipped (optional)
lettuce

1. Place agar-agar or gelatin in cold water and bring to a boil, stirring constantly until dissolved, an allow to cool.

2. Combine mayonnaise and lemon juice.

3. Place celery, onion, and shrimp or lobster in blender or food chopper and chop fine.

4. Combine with mayonnaise mixture, cream, if used, and salt and pepper and place in a wet mold or pan. Chill until firm.

Serve on lettuce.

SERVES 4

ORIENTAL CRAB

1 cup vegetable stock
juice of 2 lemons
2 teaspoons grated lemon peel
1 teaspoon arrowroot dissolved in ¼ cup cold
    water
1 teaspoon salt
2 teaspoons fresh grated ginger
2 teaspoons honey
4 scallions, cut in 1-inch pieces
2 pounds cracked crab
2 cloves garlic, crushed

1. Warm stock and lemon juice in large skillet.

2. Add lemon peel, arrowroot, salt, ginger,
honey, and scallions; simmer until scallions are
slightly cooked.

3. Add crab and cook 5 minutes.

4. Add garlic and cook until garlic is transparent.

Serve over rice.

SERVES 4

MOCK CRAB SALAD

2 pounds halibut
salt and pepper to taste
4 stalks celery, finely chopped
juice of 2—3 lemons
4 tablespoons mayonnaise
lettuce

1. Steam halibut in a steamer or colander until
it flakes; do not overcook.
2. Remove bones and flake with a fork (do not
mash).
3. Add remaining ingredients and mix gently.
Chill and serve on lettuce.

SERVES 4—6

FISH KABOBS

Marinade:

½ cup tamari soy sauce
¼ cup water
1 tablespoon curry powder
1 teaspoon ginger, grated or ground
1 bay leaf
1 onion, sliced thin
2 cloves garlic, minced
salt and pepper to taste
juice of 1 lemon
2 tablespoons oil

1½ pounds codfish, cut in chunks
3 medium tomatoes, cubed or 10 cherry
   tomatoes
2 green peppers, cubed
2 onions, cut in small chunks
½ pound mushroom caps

metal or wooden skewers

1. Combine all marinade ingredients.

2. Place fish and vegetables in bowl and cover with marinade.

3. Place bowl in a cool place, covered, for at least an hour, turning fish occasionally.

4. Place fish and vegetables alternately on skewers and broil or barbeque, basting occasionally with marinade until fish is cooked.

NOTE: Scallops or shrimp may be substituted for codfish.

SERVES 4–6

INDIAN
FISH CURRY

4 tablespoons oil
1 onion, minced
½ teaspoon fresh grated ginger
1 clove garlic, crushed
½ teaspoon turmeric
½ teaspoon mustard seeds
½ teaspoon cumin
½ teaspoon ground coriander
½ teaspoon cayenne pepper
1 teaspoon salt
pinch cinnamon
2 pounds fish fillets
½ cup stock
yogurt

1. Heat oil, add onion, stir in spices, and heat
through.

2. Add fish and stock, lower heat and cover;
simmer until fish is cooked.

3. Add yogurt and heat through or serve
yogurt on the side.

Serve over rice.

NOTE: Vegetables may be used instead of fish.

SERVES 4–6

ANCHOVY-STUFFED BASS OR TROUT

4 pounds trout or bass, backbone removed
salt and pepper to taste
juice of ½ lemon
1 can anchovies, drained and chopped
2 scallions, chopped
1 cup wheat germ or cooked brown rice
1 egg, beaten
2 stalks celery, chopped
2 tablespoons fresh chopped dill
1 tomato, chopped
⅓ cup vegetable or fish stock or water
   oil for coating

1. Preheat oven to 350°.

2. Dry fish, rub cavity with salt, and sprinkle with lemon juice.

3. Combine remaining ingredients and mix well.

4. Fill cavity loosely with mixture and fasten with toothpicks.

5. Place fish in greased baking dish; brush with oil and cover.

6. Bake at 350° for about 30 minutes; remove cover and brown slightly.

SERVES 6–8

FISH STEW

2 onions, sliced thin
½ cup oil
2 pounds fish, cut in serving pieces
1 7-ounce can tomatoes
½ cup red wine
¼ cup water
salt and pepper to taste
½ bunch parsley, chopped

1. Sauté onions in oil lightly, add fish, and sauté until lightly browned on both sides.

2. Add remaining ingredients except parsley.

3. Cook uncovered for about 45 minutes on low heat. Shake pan occasionally but do not stir.

4. Garnish with parsley.

SERVES 6–8

TROUT
ALMONDINE ORANGE

4–6 whole trouts
4 tablespoons oil
salt and pepper to taste
¾ cup blanched almonds, slivered
juice of 1 lemon
1 orange, sliced in rounds

1. Sauté fish lightly in 2 tablespoons oil and add seasoning.

2. In a separate pan, toast almonds in remaining oil until golden. Add lemon juice and orange slices and heat thoroughly.

3. Remove fish and place on platter; pour almonds and orange mixture over fish before serving.

SERVES 4–6

ROLLED FISH FILLETS WITH ASPARAGUS

6 fish fillets
juice of 1 lemon
1 onion, chopped fine
½ pound asparagus, chopped
2 tablespoons oil
1 cup wheat germ or cooked brown rice
1 tablespoon brewer's yeast (optional)
2 eggs, beaten
⅓ cup cream or milk
2 tablespoons chopped parsley
pinch each thyme and nutmeg
salt and pepper to taste

1. Preheat oven to 350°.

2. Sprinkle fillets with lemon juice.

3. Sauté onion and asparagus in oil until asparagus is tender.

4. Combine remaining ingredients and add to asparagus and onion mixture; heat thoroughly.

5. Spoon mixture onto fillets and roll; fasten with a toothpick.

6. Bake in greased pan at 350° for 15–20 minutes or until fish is flaky.

SERVES 4–6

ROE PANCAKES *

2 cups (approximately) roe from large carp,
    whitefish, or cod
2 eggs, beaten
2 carrots, grated
salt and pepper to taste
flour, matzoh meal, or cornmeal to bind
1 onion, sliced
oil for frying

1. To roe add eggs, carrots, salt, and pepper.
2. Add enough flour, matzoh meal, or cornmeal to bind to a pancake consistency.
3. Deep-fry pancakes in oil with onion slices.
Serve hot or cold.

MAKES 6 PANCAKES

* Roe is particularly high in cholesterol.

CALF LIVER ROULADES

1 onion, chopped
½ bunch parsley, chopped
½ cup bread crumbs or wheat germ
4 tablespoons oil
1 egg, beaten
¼ cup tomato juice
salt and pepper to taste
1 pound calf liver, thickly sliced, slit to form pocket

1. Preheat oven to 350°.

2. Sauté onion, parsley, bread crumbs or wheat germ in 2 tablespoons oil until lightly browned.

3. Allow to cool slightly, combine with egg, tomato juice, salt and pepper, and mix well.

4. Pack stuffing into liver and sew or secure with toothpicks.

5. Place liver in baking dish and pour 2 tablespoons oil over it.

6. Bake in 350° oven for about 40–60 minutes.

7. Cool for about 10 minutes and cut in thin slices, place on platter and pour drippings over the liver.

SERVES 4–6

FRUITY LIVER

1 pound calf liver, sliced thin
wheat germ or flour for dredging
2 tablespoons oil
1 onion, chopped
2 tablespoons tomato paste
4 apricots, fresh or canned and drained

1. Dredge liver in wheat germ or flour.

2. Heat oil and brown liver lightly on both sides.

3. Add onion and tomato paste and simmer covered for 5 minutes.

4. Add apricots and heat through.

SERVES 4

CHICKEN LIVERS MARSALA

1 pound chicken livers
1 onion, sliced
½ pound mushrooms, sliced
1 clove garlic, crushed
2 tablespoons oil
½ cup marsala wine

1. Wash chicken livers and pat dry.

2. Sauté onion, mushrooms, and garlic in oil until golden.

3. Add chicken livers and stir until browned; add marsala and simmer covered on low heat for 2–3 minutes.

SERVES 4

LIVER AND ONIONS

1 pound calf liver, cut in large cubes
flour for dredging
1 onion, sliced
1 clove garlic, minced
juice of ½ lemon
salt and pepper to taste

1. Dredge liver with flour; set aside.

2. Sauté onion and garlic until golden; add liver cubes and stir constantly until browned.

3. Add lemon juice, salt and pepper, and stir well. Serve over rice or noodles.

SERVES 4–6

LIVER KABOBS

1 pound calf liver, cut in cubes
juice of 1 lemon
1 tablespoon marjoram or oregano

Skewer liver cubes, sprinkle with lemon juice and marjoram or oregano, broil 5–10 minutes on both sides.

Serve over rice.

NOTE: Onions, mushrooms, and green pepper may also be used.

SERVES 4–6

LIVER DUMPLINGS FOR SOUP

2 eggs, separated
1 teaspoon oil
½ pound calf liver, minced fine
1 tablespoon finely chopped parsley
salt and pepper to taste
1 tablespoon bread crumbs or wheat germ
1 clove garlic, crushed

1. Beat egg yolks, add oil.

2. Mix liver, egg yolks, parsley, salt and pepper, bread crumbs or wheat germ, and garlic.

3. Beat egg whites until stiff and fold into mixture.

4. Dip teaspoon into hot soup and then drop mixture by the teaspoon into hot soup.

5. When dumplings rise to top they are cooked.

SERVES 4−6

SLAVIC
LIVER BALLS

1 pound calf liver, skinned
1 onion
1 clove garlic
2 eggs, beaten
¼ cup wheat germ, bread crumbs, or matzoh meal
3 tablespoons chopped parsley
4 tablespoons oil plus oil for frying
salt and cayenne pepper or chili powder to taste

1. Grind liver, onion, and garlic in meat grinder.

2. Add remaining ingredients and mix well.

3. Form into balls and fry on all sides until brown.

Serve with noodles as a main course or as an appetizer.

SERVES 4 –6

TURKEY FLORENTINE

4 tablespoons oil
4 tablespoons flour
2 cups stock (vegetable, chicken, or tur-
    key), boiling
salt and pepper to taste
2 pounds spinach, steamed and pureed
pinch nutmeg
sliced cooked turkey
½ cup toasted almonds

1. Heat oil, add flour gradually, stirring constantly until browned.

2. Gradually add boiling stock and continue
stirring over low heat until thick and smooth;
add salt and pepper.

3. Combine spinach with half the sauce; add
nutmeg and heat through.

4. Preheat broiler.

5. On an ovenproof platter, place a spoonful of
spinach mixture under each slice of turkey,
cover with remaining sauce, and top with almonds.

6. Brown lightly under broiler.

SERVES 6

LEMON-GARLIC CHICKEN THIGHS

1 onion, diced
1 clove garlic, crushed
2 tablespoons oil
12 chicken thighs
salt and pepper to taste
dash paprika
½ cup lemon juice
dash tamari soy sauce

1. Sauté onion and garlic in oil until golden.

2. Move onion aside and add chicken thighs; sprinkle with salt and pepper and paprika.

3. Sauté chicken until browned on both sides, sprinkle lemon juice and tamari over chicken, and simmer covered for about 20 minutes.

4. Place chicken thighs on warm serving platter and spoon browned onions over them.

SERVES 4–6

HAWAIIAN HONEYED CHICKEN LEGS

½ cup honey
½ cup tamari soy sauce
3 tablespoons oil
salt to taste
10 chicken legs
1 8-ounce can pineapple chunks (packed in
   natural juice), drained

1. Preheat broiler.

2. Mix all ingredients except chicken legs and pineapple.

3. Place chicken legs in greased shallow broiler pan.

4. Brush chicken with mixture and broil on both sides until lightly browned—about 10 minutes each side.

5. Pour remaining mixture over chicken legs and broil for a total of 30 minutes, turning occasionally.

6. A few minutes before removing from broiler, add pineapple chunks to heat through.

NOTE: This method may be used for a whole chicken cut in quarters. Some additional cooking time may be necessary.

SERVES 6–8

BAKED BREADED CHICKEN LEGS

10 chicken legs
½ pound mushrooms, chopped fine
3 cloves garlic, crushed
1 egg, beaten
2 tablespoons bread crumbs
2 tablespoons wheat germ
1 tablespoon chopped parsley
salt and pepper to taste

1. Broil chicken legs until slightly browned on both sides (when done, leave oven on at 350°).

2. Meanwhile, sauté mushrooms and garlic until tender; allow to cool slightly.

3. Combine mushrooms with remaining ingredients and roll chicken legs in mixture.

4. Bake at 350° for about 20 minutes or until chicken is cooked; dress with sauce if desired.

SERVES 6–8

CHINESE STIR-FRIED CHICKEN WITH BROCCOLI

1 onion, sliced thin
½ pound mushrooms, sliced
2 cloves garlic, crushed
4 tablespoons oil
4 chicken breasts, boned, cut in cubes
1 cup whole wheat flour
1 bunch broccoli, broken into flowerets, lightly
    steamed
salt and pepper to taste
dash powdered ginger
dash tamari soy sauce

1. Sauté onion, mushrooms, and garlic in oil until golden.

2. Dredge chicken cubes in flour and add to mushrooms; stir constantly until chicken is lightly browned.

3. Add broccoli and stir well.

4. Add salt and pepper, sprinkle with ginger, and simmer covered for 5 minutes.

5. Add tamari, mix well, and serve.

SERVES 6–8

Vegetables, Grains, and Legumes

About Grains

The difference in the measurable nutritional composition of brown rice and enriched converted white rice is considerable. Brown rice has many unknown natural B-vitamin factors that cannot be added to white rice. The occasional use of bleach and talc in the production of white rice also tips the scales in favor of natural brown rice. In addition, the whole grain is preferred because of the extra fiber that it provides, which is so important for proper digestion. Because it has not been converted, polished, bleached, and refined, it does not require the artificial enrichment added to so many modern foods. Once one becomes accustomed to the nutty-rich flavor of whole grains, the others pale by comparison.

When white rice is preferred, the converted rice should be used rather than polished or instant rice. Whenever possible, whole grains and whole grain products such as bread and pasta should be used. They not only enhance the flavor of their complementary foods such as dried beans and lentils, but boost their nutritional value as well.

So many food theories lack definitive proof, but we opt for the natural, untampered-with products. The whole food that has been polished and refined and robbed of its nutrients, only to have them artificially put back, seems a waste of time—and possibly of nutrients not yet detected and therefore impossible to replace.

Considerations for Vegetarians

A diet rich in nucleic acids has marvelous effects, but the other nutrients found in whole grains and other natural foods must also be included in a good diet, as they all support the organism and are needed for the kind of optimum health that results in deterring the aging process.

The combination of whole grains with legumes supplies the necessary nucleic acids as well as vitamins and minerals. The effect of this combination is synergistic in terms of protein. In other words, the protein derived from whole grains plus legumes equals more than the sum of each in protein content. Grains contain the amino acids absent in legumes and legumes contain the amino acids absent in grains. When they are eaten at the same meal, the resulting protein is higher than the grams of protein in each food put together. Brown rice, wheat berries, barley, kasha, rye, millet, corn, and oats may all be used to vary the vegetarian diet and can be used interchangeably in many recipes.

The combinations of foods that must be included in a vegetarian diet are:

grains with legumes (lentils, beans, peas, and peanuts)
grains with dairy products (milk, cheese, etc.)
legumes with seeds and nuts

The recipes that follow lend themselves to these combinations and in many instances include them.

It is essential that vegetarians be aware that giving up animal protein is only the beginning of vegetarianism. Close attention must be paid to good nutrition. Foods should be as free of additives and pesticides as possible, and some raw foods should be included in the diet. A daily multivitamin that includes B_{12} is very important, and it would be wise to study the possibility of further vitamin-mineral supplements to compensate for the depletion of these elements from the soil in which our food is grown.

Dr. Rudolph Alsleben, publisher of the nutritional magazine called *Answer* and practitioner of orthomolecular medicine, believes that optimum food no longer exists and some supplementation is essential. He is not alone in this view. The polluted condition of our planet makes it critical that we learn to be aware of our personal nutritional needs in terms of diet and supplements. An important nutritional supplement highly recommended by Dr. Frank is brewer's yeast. Dr. Frank states that aside from the vitamins and minerals it provides, brewer's yeast is very high in nucleic acids. He recommends it as a supplement for nonvegetarians as well. The mild, debittered variety is more palatable than the strong undebittered variety. However, Dr. Frank prefers the latter, so you must make the choice.

We know that the following recipes will be of special interest to vegetarians, and hope that others will find them an interesting and delicious introduction to a more varied and nutritious diet.

Basic Preparation of Grains

Boiled

The simplest method of cooking brown rice is to use two parts water to one part rice. Place rice in colander under running water to clean rice thoroughly. Put rice in cold salted water in a heavy pot with a tight-fitting lid. Bring to a boil uncovered, lower heat and cover. Simmer for about 45 minutes until rice is tender and water is absorbed. Do not lift cover or stir rice during cooking. Stock, soup, or sauce may be substituted for water.

Sautéed

This method is excellent for other grains, such as barley, millet, kasha, and wheat berries, as well as brown rice. Heat some oil in a heavy skillet, add the grain (if desired, onions and/or mushrooms may be added), and sauté lightly, stirring constantly until golden. Lower heat and add 2 parts boiling water or stock; cover and simmer for about 45 minutes until grain is tender and liquid is absorbed. Add more liquid if needed. Do not stir during cooking.

Baked

Any grain may be baked plain or with vegetables. Lightly sauté grain in a small amount of oil. Add 2½ parts boiling water or stock. Cover and bake at 325°–350° for about an hour or until all liquid is absorbed. If necessary, add more liquid. If using vegetables, either combine with grain or place on top (dry vegetables like carrots and turnips require a bit more liquid). Cut vegetables in large pieces so that they will not get mushy.

Steamed

Processed grains such as couscous and bulgur need not be boiled. Put bulgur in a large bowl, cover with 2 parts boiling water or stock and let stand until all liquid is absorbed. Couscous should be wet down, drained, and steamed in a colander or steamer placed over stock and vegetables until cooked. Couscous may also be cooked by stirring one part couscous into 2 parts boiling water or stock. Return to boil, simmer for about 3 minutes covered, remove from heat and allow to stand covered until all liquid is absorbed.

OATMEAL-CHEESE PUDDING

1 onion, chopped
2 scallions, cut in small pieces
2 tablespoons oil
1½ cups rolled oats
1½ cups vegetable stock
2 eggs, beaten
½ pound Cheddar cheese, grated
1 teaspoon salt
pinch pepper
½ teaspoon sage

1. Preheat oven to 350°.

2. Sauté onion and scallions in oil until golden.

3. Add oats and stock, bring to a boil and lower heat, cook until thick—about 10 minutes.

4. Remove from heat and mix in eggs, cheese, and seasonings.

5. Pour into greased baking dish and bake at 350° for 45 minutes or until brown.

SERVES 4–6

CHEESY SPINACH-RICE CASSEROLE

¾ cup cooked rice
1 pound spinach, chopped and steamed until wilted (chard or any other leafy green may be used)
2 onions, chopped
1 clove garlic, crushed
dash tamari soy sauce
½ cup vegetable stock
¼ cup grated cheese

1. Preheat oven to 350°.
2. Mix all ingredients except cheese.
3. Place in greased baking dish.
4. Sprinkle cheese over mixture.
5. Bake at 350° for about 20 minutes.

SERVES 4–6

RICE AND
SPINACH PATTIES

1 onion, chopped
1½ cups brown rice
2 tablespoons oil
3 cups water or vegetable stock, boiling
salt to taste
pinch rosemary
3 tablespoons grated cheese (Parmesan, Swiss,
   Cheddar, etc.)
1 tablespoon butter (optional)
2 eggs, beaten
¼ pound raw spinach, chopped
2 tablespoons whole wheat flour or wheat
   germ
oil for frying patties

1. Sauté onion and rice in oil until golden.

2. Add stock or water, salt, rosemary, and
cover; simmer over low heat 40–45 minutes
until all moisture is absorbed by the rice.

3. Mix in cheese and butter.

4. Combine with eggs and spinach, shape into
patties, dip in flour or wheat germ and fry in oil
until light brown on both sides.

SERVES 4

RICE AND
LENTIL BALLS

1½ cups cooked brown rice
¾ cup cooked lentils
3 scallions, cut in ½-inch slices
2 tablespoons toasted sesame seeds
nori seaweed sheets (optional)

1. Mix rice and lentils.

2. Wet hands in cold salted water and form mixture into small balls. Keep hands wet to avoid sticking.

3. Insert a piece of scallion into each ball.

4. Roll each ball in sesame seeds.

5. Toast nori lightly until green color turns black; wrap around each ball.

NOTE: May also be served as an appetizer.

SERVES 4

STUFFED SQUASH SUPREME

1 onion, sliced
2 tablespoons oil
1 cup cooked rice
2 tablespoons raisins
½ cup roasted nuts or seeds
¼ teaspoon salt
1 cup cooked fish or canned salmon
2 squash (acorn or butternut), cut in half, seeds scooped out

1. Preheat oven to 350°.

2. Sauté onion in oil until lightly browned; add rice and stir well.

3. Mix in raisins, nuts or seeds, salt, and fish.

4. Sprinkle squash with salt and fill cavity with stuffing.

5. Place in pan with ½ inch of water on bottom.

6. Bake covered at 350° for about 1 hour until squash is tender.

NOTE: Leftover stuffing may be used as a side dish.

SERVES 4

MIDDLE EASTERN BULGUR AND CHICK PEAS

1 clove garlic, crushed
1 onion, chopped
1 tablespoon anise seeds
salt to taste
2 tablespoons oil
1 cup bulgur wheat, soaked in 2 cups hot
   water for ½ hour or until liquid is absorbed
1 cup cooked chick peas
1 teaspoon fresh chopped mint leaves
½ cup water, boiling

1. Sauté garlic, onion, anise, and salt in oil until onion is lightly browned.

2. Add bulgur, chick peas, and mint; mix well.

3. Add ½ cup boiling water and simmer about 5 minutes.

May be served hot or cold.

SERVES 4–6

PILAF

1 onion, chopped
2 tablespoons oil
1 cup bulgur wheat
1 cup pignoli (pine nuts)
½ cup currants
salt and pepper to taste
pinch coriander
2 cups vegetable stock, boiling

1. Sauté onion in oil until golden.

2. Add bulgur and toast lightly.

3. Add pignoli, currants, and seasonings, and stir lightly.

4. Add boiling stock, cover, and remove from heat.

Let stand 5 minutes before serving so that all liquid is absorbed.

SERVES 4–6

MOCK
MASHED POTATOES

1 cup millet
3 cups stock, boiling
½ head cauliflower, broken into flowerets
2 tablespoons butter
salt and pepper to taste
1 tablespoon chopped dill
½ cup skim milk (optional)
3 tablespoons grated Cheddar cheese

1. Add millet to boiling stock, return to boil,
lower heat and simmer covered until liquid is
absorbed and millet is soft—about 45 minutes.

2. Steam cauliflower until tender.

3. Mix cauliflower and millet with electric hand
mixer until smooth.

4. Add butter, salt, pepper, dill, milk if desired,
and mix in cheese.

SERVES 4–6

KASHA AND MUSHROOMS

1 cup kasha (buckwheat groats)
1 egg, beaten
3 tablespoons oil
2 cups stock, boiling
1 onion, chopped
½ pound mushrooms, chopped
salt and pepper to taste

1. Mix kasha with beaten egg.

2. Brown kasha in 2 tablespoons oil, stirring constantly, until egg is dry. Lower heat, add boiling stock, and cover.

3. In separate skillet, brown onion and mushrooms in 1 tablespoon oil and add to kasha.

4. Simmer covered over low heat until liquid is absorbed.

Serve with basic brown sauce or tahini sauce (see Sauces).

SERVES 4–6

INDIAN DAL

1½ cups lentils, washed and picked over
4 cups water
2 tablespoons oil
2 cloves garlic, crushed
salt to taste
pinch cayenne pepper

1. Boil lentils in water until very soft, adding more water if needed.

2. Heat oil in skillet, add garlic, and lower heat.

3. Remove lentils from water with slotted spoon and place in oil.

4. Stir and mash lentils in oil with a wooden spoon; add enough water from boiled lentils to adjust consistency.

5. Add salt and cayenne pepper.

Serve with rice and a side dish of yogurt.

NOTE: A pinch of cumin powder adds an exotic flavor.

SERVES 4 – 6

LENTIL LOAF

1½ cups lentils, washed and picked over
1 large onion, diced
2 cloves garlic, crushed
½ cup chopped parsley
2 tablespoons oil
½ cup wheat germ
½ cup bread crumbs
2 tablespoons fresh chopped dill
pinch thyme, coriander, celery seed, and chili
    powder
salt and pepper to taste
1 egg, beaten
juice of 1 lemon
dash tamari soy sauce

1. Preheat oven to 350°.

2. Cook lentils in water to cover until tender—
about 45 minutes.

3. Meanwhile, sauté onion, garlic, and parsley
in oil.

4. Add wheat germ and bread crumbs.

5 Mash lentils with some of the cooking liquid;
add seasonings. Mixture should be moist. Add
remaining ingredients.

6. Combine lentil and onion mixtures thoroughly.

7. Bake in greased loaf pan at 350° for about
30 minutes or until bottom is brown.

May be served hot or cold.

SERVES 4–6

LENTIL SHEPHERD'S PIE

1 cup lentils, washed and picked over
1 onion, chopped
1 stalk celery, chopped
1 clove garlic, chopped
2 cups vegetable stock
1 tomato, chopped
1 teaspoon salt
1 teaspoon basil
4 potatoes
½ cup skim milk
1 tablespoon oil
pepper to taste
½ cup sesame seeds

1. Preheat oven to 375°.

2. Cook lentils, onion, celery, and garlic in stock over low heat until lentils are soft but not dry (add more liquid if needed); add tomato, salt, and basil and heat through.

3. Meanwhile, boil potatoes and mash with milk, oil, and pepper.

4. Layer a greased baking dish with lentil mixture and spoon potatoes on top; sprinkle sesame seeds over potatoes and bake at 375° for about 30 minutes or until potatoes are browned.

NOTE: Keep mixture moist so it does not dry out while baking.

SERVES 4 –6

LENTIL BURGERS

1½ cups lentils, washed and picked over
3 cups water
1 large onion, minced
2 cloves garlic, minced
2 tablespoons oil
¼ cup whole wheat flour
¼ cup sunflower seeds
2 tablespoons nut meal (almond, sunflower,
   etc.) or wheat germ
salt and pepper to taste
oil for frying burgers

1. Cook lentils in water until soft—about 35
minutes.

2. Sauté onion and garlic in oil.

3. Drain lentils; reserve water.

4. Combine all ingredients except water and oil
for frying.

5. Form into patties, using lentil water to adjust
consistency if necessary.

6. Fry in oil on both sides until browned.

NOTE: The patties may be broiled or baked. Add
2 tablespoons oil to mixture, form patties, and
bake in preheated 350° oven or broil until
brown. Serve with tomato or brown sauce if
desired.

SERVES 4–6

BAKED BEANS

1 cup raw beans (soy, pinto, or kidney),
   soaked 6 hours
2 tomatoes, chopped
1 sweet pepper, diced
2 tablespoons oil
2 tablespoons honey or molasses
2 tablespoons miso paste, diluted in ½ cup
   water
1 tablespoon cider vinegar
pinch basil
½ teaspoon cayenne pepper
salt to taste
½ cup vegetable stock

1. Preheat oven to 325°−350°.

2. Combine beans and vegetables and place in baking dish.

3. Mix remaining ingredients and stir into bean mixture.

4. Cover and bake at 325°−350° for 2−3 hours or until beans are cooked.

NOTE: Add more stock to beans if needed.

SERVES 6−8

SPICY BEETS

1½ pounds beets, steamed (leaves optional)
1 large red onion, sliced thin
1 tablespoon Dijon mustard
2 teaspoons lemon juice
4 tablespoons yogurt
salt and pepper to taste
½ teaspoon ground cumin

1. Allow beets to cool; peel and slice thin.

2. Place in bowl and add onion.

3. Blend remaining ingredients well and combine with beets.

Serve chilled.

SERVES 4

CURRIED BEETS

1 onion, diced
1 stalk celery, sliced
1 apple, cored, peeled, and diced
2 tablespoons oil
2 tablespoons whole wheat flour
2 cups stock, boiling
1 tablespoon curry powder
1 pound beets, washed well and sliced thin;
     leaves chopped (optional)

1. Sauté onion, celery, and apple in oil until onion is transparent.

2. Add flour, stirring constantly.

3. When flour begins to brown, lower heat and slowly add stock and curry powder while stirring to maintain smoothness.

4. Add sliced beets and simmer about 25 minutes or until beets are cooked; add more stock if needed.

SERVES 4

LEMON BEETS

1 pound beets, sliced
juice of 2 lemons
1 teaspoon grated lemon rind
½ teaspoon ground cloves
1 teaspoon honey
salt to taste
1 teaspoon arrowroot dissolved in ½ cup of
    beet liquid

1. Steam beets; reserve liquid.

2. In separate pan, combine lemon juice and rind, cloves, honey, salt, and arrowroot.

3. Simmer over low heat until thickened; serve over beets.

SERVES 4 – 6

BRAISED ASPARAGUS

½ cup sunflower seeds (hulled)
1 clove garlic, crushed
1 tablespoon oil
1 pound asparagus, tough ends removed
salt and pepper to taste
dash lemon juice

1. Toast seeds and garlic in oil until lightly browned.

2. Add asparagus, salt and pepper, and sauté until soft but firm.

3. Sprinkle lemon juice over asparagus.

Serve hot.

SERVES 4

SAUTÉED VEGETABLES ORIENTALE

1 large onion, sliced thin
1 tablespoon oil
½ head cauliflower or broccoli, broken in
   flowerets
2 carrots, sliced thin
½ cup cooked chick peas
salt and pepper to taste
dill (optional)
grated ginger (optional)
dash tamari soy sauce

1. Sauté onion in oil until transparent.

2. Add remaining ingredients, except tamari.

3. Stir and fry over medium heat for a few minutes; cover and simmer over low heat for 2 or 3 minutes, depending on how crunchy you like the vegetables.

4. Turn off heat, add tamari and stir.

Serve on a bed of rice or whole wheat noodles.

NOTE: Any single vegetable or combination of vegetables may be prepared this way; always use the onion.

SERVES 4–6

SPINACH LASAGNA

2 onions, chopped
2 cloves garlic, minced
2 tablespoons oil
2 pounds spinach, chopped
1 pound ricotta cheese
¼ pound Parmesan cheese, grated
2 eggs, beaten
salt and pepper to taste
pinch oregano
1 pound whole wheat lasagne noodles
½ pound mozzarella cheese, sliced thin
2 quarts sardine tomato sauce (see Sauces; omit sardines if desired)

1. Preheat oven to 350°.

2. Sauté onions and garlic in oil until golden; add spinach and sauté lightly.

3. Combine onion-spinach mixture with ricotta, Parmesan, and eggs; mix well; add seasonings.

4. Cook noodles *al dente*.

5. In a large greased baking dish, layer noodles, ricotta-spinach mixture, mozzarella slices, and tomato sauce; repeat layers and top with sauce. Sprinkle additional Parmesan on top.

6. Bake at 350° for about 40 minutes, covered. Remove cover and brown for a few minutes.

SERVES 6–8

MUSHROOM AND SPINACH PIE

1 onion, chopped coarsely
½ pound mushrooms, chopped
1 tablespoon oil
½ pound spinach, chopped fine
pastry crust (Any standard pastry crust will do.)
4 eggs, beaten
1 cup milk
1 cup cream
½ teaspoon dried hot pepper
salt and pepper to taste
dash nutmeg

1. Preheat oven to 350°.

2. Sauté onion and mushrooms in oil.

3. Steam spinach until wilted.

4. Combine spinach with onions and mushrooms and fill crust.

5. Mix eggs, milk, cream, and seasonings; pour over spinach mixture.

6. Bake at 350° for about 40 minutes or until mixture sets.

NOTE: Cauliflower or asparagus may be used instead of spinach.

SERVES 4

Index